MIND BENDERS® A3

DEDUCTIVE THINKING SKILLS

SERIES TITLES

Mind Benders® Warm Up, Mind Benders® A1, Mind Benders® A2, Mind Benders® A3, Mind Benders® A4, Mind Benders® B1, Mind Benders® B2, Mind Benders® B3, Mind Benders® B4, Mind Benders® C1, Mind Benders® C2, Mind Benders® C3

ANITA HARNADEK

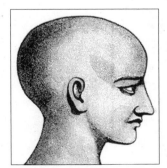

© 2000, 1981
THE CRITICAL THINKING COMPANY
www.CriticalThinking.com
P.O. Box 448 • Pacific Grove • CA 93950-0448
Phone 800-458-4849 • FAX 831-393-3277
ISBN 0-89455-121-3
Printed in the United States of America

TABLE OF CONTENTS

TEACHER SUGGESTIONS

PURPOSE

Students having wide ranges of ability, motivation, and achievement seem to be remarkably attracted to Mind Benders® problems. Students who may or may not try to use deductive reasoning for ordinary classwork or homework seem to think Mind Benders® are fun, not work. So the purpose of the MIND BENDERS® series is to give each student what (s)he wants—fun, a happy diversion from routine—while at the same time forcing the student to organize sets of clues—some direct, some indirect—and reach logical conclusions by using pure deductive reasoning.

GENERAL INFORMATION

There are twelve exercise books in this series:

WARM-UP MIND BENDERS®

MIND BENDERS® A1

MIND BENDERS® A2

MIND BENDERS® A3

MIND BENDERS® A4

MIND BENDERS® B1

MIND BENDERS® B2

MIND BENDERS® B3

MIND BENDERS® B4

MIND BENDERS® C1

MIND BENDERS® C2

MIND BENDERS® C3

The **A** series is easy, **B** is medium, and **C** is hard.

Although most of the problems in WARM UP MIND BENDERS® vary from extremely easy to easy, there are a handful in the medium range. The idea of the problems in the warmup book is to give the students practice in using deductive reasoning in very simple situations before presenting them with more clues to use and with clues which are more subtle, as in the other MIND BENDERS® books.

Since some teachers will need more problems for their students than other teachers, more than one book is available in each of the A, B, and C categories. Within a category, there is no substantial difference in difficulty between the books offered. (For example, a teacher who needs only 15 problems at the easy level may order any of the four MIND BENDERS® books in the A series.)

See page iv for general comments about assumptions that can be made from clues.

HELPFUL HINTS ABOUT SOLVING MIND BENDERS®

Most Mind Benders® in the A, B, and C categories are solved more easily if a chart is used than if the solver simply makes notes about the clues given. To help students solve the problems, each Mind Bender® is accompanied by a chart made especially for that particular problem.

See page vi for a step-by-step explanation of using charts to solve Mind Bender® problems, including the way each chart looks after each step. None of the problems used there are used as exercises in any of the MIND BENDERS® books.

The instructions (in highly abbreviated form, of course) are these: To fill in a chart, make a notation in each square which is eliminated by a clue. (The notation might be the clue number or the word "no," for example.) When there is only one blank square left in a row (or column) within a category, then "X" that square. Then note the elimination of all the other squares in the matching column (or row). When a chart contains three or more categories, then either the elimination of a square or the "X"ing of a square may also give you more information about previous clues. (For example, if you know that Mr. Brown owns the red car and you have just discovered that the Chevrolet is not the red car, then you have also discovered that Mr. Brown does not own the Chevrolet.)

SOLUTIONS

Note 1: Each problem has only one solution. If the notation used for eliminations is simply a "no," then the completed chart will have an "X" for each combination named in the solutions given below, and the chart will have a "no" everywhere else. If the notation used for elimination is a clue number, however, then the completed chart may vary from one student to another. (This is because eliminations can sometimes be made in different orders.)

Note 2: If your solutions do not agree with those given, refer to the Examples and Step-by-Step Procedures on page 31 for information on how to use charts to solve Mind Benders® problems.

About the Clues in MIND BENDERS®

In general, the MIND BENDERS® assume that you will, when using the clues, apply three guidelines unless a problem leads you to believe otherwise:

1.   Think of everyday situations rather than of highly unusual exceptions.

2.   Think of standards which are generally acceptable to U.S. society as a whole.

3.   Use common sense and context in deciding what the clues mean.

Following are examples:

a.   Assume that only males have male names (John, Robert, Dave) and only females have female names (Mary, Jennifer, Cathy). But be careful not to make such assumptions about unisex names (Pat, Chris).

b.   Assume that typical U.S. social relationships apply. For example, if John is engaged to Mary, you may assume they know each other. You may assume that very close relatives know each other.

c.   Don't assume that rare age relationships may apply. For example, don't assume that a 7 year old might be a college graduate, or that a parent might be younger than his or her adopted child. On the other hand, although most cases of age may be in one direction, enough cases in the other direction may exist so that these would not be considered especially unusual. For example, a husband may be a good deal younger than his wife, or a 45 year old may get the mumps.

d.   Assume that animals are of normal size. For example, "a horse" is not "a pygmy horse"; "a small dog" is smaller than a goat; a "large dog" is simply one of the larger breeds of dogs. If a problem talks about a cat and a fox, assume that the cat is smaller than the fox. Do not think that maybe the cat is fully grown and the fox is a few weeks old.

e.   Assume that animals are called by their usual names within the context. For example, if John and Mary have a pet dog and a pet cat, assume that the cat is an ordinary household cat, rather than maybe a tiger or a leopard.

f.   Don't look for tricky situations. For example, suppose the problem has four houses in a row (and no other houses). And suppose Debby lives next door to Gary. Don't assume that Debby or Gary might live in a garage between two of the houses. That is, assume that they live in two of the four houses in the problem.

g.   Assume that typical U.S. social situations apply. For example, if John went on a date with Abbott, assume two things: (1) Abbott is a female; (2) neither John nor Abbott is married, since (a) when a married couple go out, we do not call it a "date," and (b) if either one is married to someone else, then it is not typical for him or her to be dating someone.

h.   Pay attention to what the clues say. For example, suppose a problem has four people, and suppose one clue says, "Cathy and the dentist ride to work together in a car pool." Also suppose another clue says, "Brown, who does not know any of the other three people, is not the typist." Then you should deduce that neither Cathy nor the dentist is Brown.

i.   Exact wording to eliminate ambiguities sometimes makes a clue too long. The clue is then shortened to the point where it is unambiguous to most people, but some people would still recognize ambiguities and object to the wording. In such cases, consider the context and the intent of the clue. As examples:

(1) "Neither Bob nor Young lives in the white house," means, "Bob is not Young, and Bob does not live in the white house, and Young does not live in the white house."

(2) "John and Abbott went bowling with Dave and Smith," means, "Four different people went bowling together. One of these was John, one was Abbott, one was Dave, and one was Smith."

(3) "Jane doesn't know either Mary or the artist," means, "Jane doesn't know Mary, and Jane doesn't know the artist, and Mary is not the artist."

(4) "Neither Carol nor Bill went to the party, and Norris didn't go, either," refers to three different people.

(5) In general, "neither ... nor" and "either ... or" sentences will refer to separate things, as in the above examples. Just plain "or" sentences, however, are sometimes less definite, as in this example: "Neither Becky nor Jackson has the dog or is the secretary." Here, Becky and Jackson are different people, but we aren't sure that the person who has the dog is not also the secretary.

MISCELLANEOUS INFORMATION

Most of the problems you will find that are similar to these Mind Benders® seem to be good ones, but you may run into some that could be better. Here are examples of clues from such problems:

1. One clue reads, "Abbott told Baker that he could beat her at weight lifting." You can't tell which one is the man and which is the woman from this sentence. It may be that a man (Abbott) is claiming that he can beat a woman (Baker) at weight lifting, or it may be that a woman (Abbott) is claiming that a man (Baker) can beat her at weight lifting.

2. One clue tells you that Abbott is single, and another clue refers to John's children. You don't know whether or not the writer thinks that single people don't have children. (Maybe he adopted children.)

3. Some problems have contradictory clues. I once saw a problem in which one clue said that Abbott spent all of his spare time doing one thing (reading, for example), and another clue said that John was doing something else with his friends (watching TV, for example). So I marked on the chart that John was not Abbott. But a few minutes later I found the problem to be unsolvable, so I looked at the solution which came with it. The solution showed that John was Abbott.

1. Lots of Rocks

A boulder, a cobble, and a pebble are in a gorge, a lake, and a valley. The rock in the valley is larger than the cobble. The cobble is not in the lake.

Where is each rock?

2. Class President

Agnes, Betsy, Cornelius, and Dexter each voted for a different person for class president (Grant, Houh, McGuire, Sterling).

Match them up from the clues below.

1. The boy who voted for McGuire is older than the person who voted for Sterling and is younger than Dexter.

2. The person who voted for Houh is taller than Betsy and the person who voted for Grant.

3. Agnes didn't vote for Houh.

Chart for Problem 2

	Grant	Houh	McGuire	Sterling
Agnes				
Betsy				
Cornelius				
Dexter				

3. School Attendance

Dana, Ephraim, John, and Martha attend four different schools (Adams, Carver, King, Lincoln).

Match each person with the school attended.

1. Dana is the cousin of the girl who attends Lincoln.

2. Ephraim's school played baseball against King last week.

3. The girl who attends Carver used to live next door to a boy named Nelson.

Chart for Problem 3

	Adams	Carver	King	Lincoln
Dana				
Ephraim				
John				
Martha				

4. Army Officers

Atherton, Barron, Randall, and Weissman are in the army. Their ranks are colonel, general, lieutenant, and major. (From low to high, the ranks are lieutenant, major, colonel, general.)

Find each person's rank from the clues below.

1. Barron's rank is higher than Weissman's and lower than Randall's.

2. Weissman is not the lieutenant.

Chart for Problem 4

	colonel	general	lieutenant	major
Atherton				
Barron				
Randall				
Weissman				

5. Spelling Contest

Bobby, Jackie, Mickey, and Pat finished in first, second, third, and fourth places in a spelling contest.

Figure out how each person did in the contest and whether the person is a boy or a girl.

1. The person who finished in first place does not know Jackie, but he knows her little brother.

2. Pat studied the spelling list with Mickey and the other girl, but both did better in the contest than he did.

3. Jackie did better in the contest than Mickey did.

Chart for Problem 5

	1st	2nd	3rd	4th
Bobby				
Jackie				
Mickey				
Pat				

6. Old-Time Radio Shows

Amherst, Bartlett, Croft, Davies, and Enders each listened to a rebroadcast of an old radio program ("Fibber McGee and Molly," "The Green Hornet," "Jack Benny," "The Lone Ranger," "The Shadow").

Match them up from the clues below.

1. Bartlett listened to a program about the Old West.

2. Neither Amherst nor Croft listened to either comedy program.

3. Enders didn't listen to the Jack Benny program.

4. Amherst didn't listen to "The Green Hornet."

Chart for Problem 6

	Fibber McGee and Molly	The Green Hornet	Jack Benny	The Lone Ranger	The Shadow
Amherst					
Bartlett					
Croft					
Davies					
Enders					

7.   Home with the Animals

Lauren, Norman, and Peter are a cat, a dog, and a mouse. They live in a barn, a garage, and a house.

Figure out who is what and who lives where.

1. The cat, who is not Peter, wishes he could eat tuna fish every day.

2. Lauren is larger than the animal who lives in the house.

3. The animal who lives in the barn is angry at the mouse, who tricked him yesterday.

4. Lauren is a female, and the other two animals are males.

Chart for Problem 7

	cat	dog	mouse	barn	garage	house
Lauren						
Norman						
Peter						
barn						
garage						
house						

8.   Students and Subjects

Five students in a class (Bob, Cathy, Dan, Ed, Faye) are each the best at a certain subject (arithmetic, geography, handwriting, reading, spelling).

Match up the student and the subject from the clues below.

1. Dan, Cathy, and the student who is the best at spelling walked to school with Ed and the student who is the best at geography.

2. Cathy and the student who is the best at handwriting had lunch at school with Bob and the student who is the best at geography.

3. Dan and the student who is the best at handwriting walked home from school with the student who is the best at reading.

Chart for Problem 8

	arithmetic	geography	hand-writing	reading	spelling
Bob					
Cathy					
Dan					
Ed					
Faye					

9. Company Presidents

Figure out who (Jorgenson, Kiley, Litton, Tyler) is the president of which company (Big Co., Giant Corp., Mammoth Co., Super Co.).

1. Kiley doesn't know the president of Mammoth Co. but has heard of him.

2. Jorgenson used to work at Giant Corp. but then got a better offer from the company where she's working now.

3. The president of Big Co. and his wife go golfing several times each year.

4. Litton, who has been with the same company for twenty years, worked her way up from the bottom.

Chart for Problem 9

	Big Co.	Giant Corp.	Mammoth Co.	Super Co.
Jorgenson				
Kiley				
Litton				
Tyler				

10. Animals at the Zoo

Five animals (aardvark, bear, cheetah, elephant, zebra) live in zoos in different cities (Detroit, Houston, Omaha, San Diego, Tacoma).

Match up each animal with the zoo where it lives.

1. The animal in the Tacoma zoo, which is not the aardvark, can climb trees.

2. The striped animal is not in a zoo in the southern part of the country.

3. The fastest animal is in the San Diego zoo.

4. The elephant is older than the animal in the Detroit zoo and younger than the animal in Houston's zoo.

Chart for Problem 10

	Detroit	Houston	Omaha	San Diego	Tacoma
aardvark					
bear					
cheetah					
elephant					
zebra					

11. What's in a Name?

Art, Bob, Cathy, Debbie, and Harold have last names of Green, Ingram, Jones, King, and Lathem.

Match the first names with the last names.

1. Jones is older than either of the other men but is younger than Green.

2. Debbie is younger than Harold but older than King and Art.

3. Ingram is younger than Lathem.

Chart for Problem 11

	Green	Ingram	Jones	King	Lathem
Art					
Bob					
Cathy					
Debbie					
Harold					

12. Choice of Careers

Antonia, Colleen, Emmanuel, and Gustave, whose last names are Dewey, Hamilton, Kennedy, and Shaw, are a biologist, a flight attendant, a magician, and a plasterer.

Match up everything from the clues below.

1. The man who is the flight attendant, who is not Kennedy or Dewey, is 25.

2. Kennedy, who is not the magician, is older than Hamilton and is younger than Emmanuel.

3. Shaw, who is not Antonia, is very good at her work, which is not part of the building industry.

4. Antonia is not the plasterer.

Chart for Problem 12

	Dewey	Hamilton	Kennedy	Shaw	biologist	flight attendant	magician	plasterer
Antonia								
Colleen								
Emmanuel								
Gustave								
biologist								
flight attendant								
magician								
plasterer								

13. When Were They Born?

Two girls and two boys (Alexander, Bertha, Glenn, Hiroko), whose last names are Kraft, Loring, Silverman, and Tyndall, were born in different months (February, January, May, October) of the same year.

Match up everything from the clues below.

1. Glenn was born after Tyndall and before Hiroko.

2. Bertha is older than Kraft and younger than Loring.

3. Silverman is not the youngest, and Tyndall is not the oldest.

Chart for Problem 13

	Kraft	Loring	Silverman	Tyndall	January	February	May	October
Alexander								
Bertha								
Glenn								
Hiroko								
January								
February								
May								
October								

14. Shopping Trip

Annette, Carlo, Duane, and Edith, whose last names are Menzotti, Northrop, Oliver, and Preston, went shopping. They bought a bathing suit, gloves, a jacket, and slacks.

Match up everything from the clues below.

1. Annette went shopping with Oliver and the person who bought the bathing suit.

2. Duane knows neither Northrop nor the person who bought the slacks.

3. Edith, who isn't Oliver, had lunch with Preston and the person who bought the gloves.

Chart for Problem 14

	Menzotti	Northrop	Oliver	Preston	bathing suit	gloves	jacket	slacks
Annette								
Carlo								
Duane								
Edith								
bathing suit								
gloves								
jacket								
slacks								

SOLUTIONS

GENERAL COMMENTS ABOUT SOLUTIONS

There is more than one way to approach the solution of most Mind Benders®. For example, if a problem has five clues, you might choose to apply clue 4 first and clue 2 second, while the solution here for that problem uses clue 3 first and clue 5 second. Since there is only one final answer to the problem, the order in which the clues are used does not affect the final answer.

In order to understand a solution here, it is necessary that you have a copy of the problem to refer to while you are reading the solution. Also, it is definitely suggested, particularly for the problems in the B and C series, that you write down the findings as you go through a solution in order to help keep track of the rationale. For example, suppose a problem uses first and last names and occupations of three people. Before you start reading the solution here, write down the first names, leaving space to fill in the last names and occupations:

Bernard

Catherine

Donald

Then this is what your notes will look like as you read through (part of) the detailed solution, "Smith is a man (2) but isn't Donald (4), so he is Bernard."

Bernard Smith

Catherine

Donald

"The TV repairer is a man (3) but isn't Smith (3), so he is Donald."

Bernard Smith

Catherine

Donald,   TV repairer

Notice in the above example that clue numbers are referred to in parentheses.

DETAILED SOLUTIONS

1.

ROCK	LOCATION
boulder	valley
cobble	gorge
pebble	lake

A pebble is smaller than a cobble, so the pebble is not the rock in the valley. Since the rock in the valley is not the cobble, it is the boulder. The cobble isn't in the lake, so the pebble is, and so the cobble is in the gorge.

2.

STUDENT	CANDIDATE
Agnes	Grant
Betsy	Sterling
Cornelius	McGuire
Dexter	Houh

A boy voted for McGuire (1), but he isn't Dexter (1), so he is Cornelius. Betsy didn't vote for Houh or Grant (2), so she voted for Sterling. Agnes didn't vote for Houh (3), so Dexter did, and Agnes voted for Grant.

3.

STUDENT	SCHOOL
Dana	Carver
Ephraim	Adams
John	King
Martha	Lincoln

There are two girls in the problem (1, 3), so Dana is a girl. The girl who attends Lincoln isn't Dana (1), so she is Martha. Then the girl who attends Carver (3) is Dana. Ephraim doesn't go to King (2), so John does, and so Ephraim goes to Adams.

4.

NAME	RANK
Atherton	lieutenant
Barron	colonel
Randall	general
Weissman	major

Weissman is not the colonel or the general (1) or the lieutenant (2), so Weissman is the major. Then Barron is the colonel and Randall is the general (1), so Atherton is the lieutenant.

5.

NAME	SEX	PLACE
Bobby	boy	first
Jackie	girl	second
Mickey	girl	third
Pat	boy	fourth

Pat is a boy (2). Then Mickey and one other person are girls (2). Jackie is a girl (1), so Bobby is a boy. A boy finished in first place (1), but he isn't Pat (2), so he is Bobby. Then Pat finished in fourth place (2). Jackie finished in second place and Mickey finished in third place (3).

6.

NAME	SHOW
Amherst	"The Shadow"
Bartlett	"The Lone Ranger"
Croft	"The Green Hornet"
Davies	"Jack Benny"
Enders	"Fibber McGee and Molly"

Bartlett listened to "The Lone Ranger" (1). Amherst and Croft listened to "The Green Hornet" and "The Shadow" (2), but Amherst didn't listen to "The Green Hornet" (4), so Croft did, and so Amherst listened to "The Shadow." Enders didn't listen to "Jack Benny" (3), so Davies did, and so Enders listened to "Fibber McGee and Molly."

7.

NAME	ANIMAL	DWELLING
Lauren	dog	garage
Norman	cat	barn
Peter	mouse	house

Lauren is female (4) and is not the cat (1, male) or the mouse (2), so Lauren is the dog. Lauren does not live in the house (2) or in the barn (3, male), so Lauren lives in the garage. Peter is not the cat (1), so Peter is the mouse. Peter doesn't live in the barn (3), so he lives in the house. This leaves Norman to be the cat and to live in the barn.

8.

STUDENT	SUBJECT
Bob	spelling
Cathy	reading
Dan	arithmetic
Ed	handwriting
Faye	geography

Bob and Faye, the only two not mentioned by name in clue 1, are the best at spelling and geography (1). Bob isn't the best at geography (2), so Faye is, and Bob is the best at spelling. Dan isn't the best at handwriting or reading (3), so his subject is arithmetic. Cathy isn't the best at handwriting (2), so Ed is, and Cathy is the best at reading.

9.

PRESIDENT	COMPANY
Jorgenson	Super Co.
Kiley	Big Co.
Litton	Giant Corp.
Tyler	Mammoth Co.

Jorgenson (2) and Litton (4) are females, whereas the presidents of Mammoth Co. (1) and Big Co. (3) are males. Jorgenson doesn't work at Giant Corp. (2), so Litton does, and so Jorgenson is the president of Super Co. Kiley is not the president of Mammoth Co. (1), so Tyler is, and Kiley is the president of Big Co.

10.

ANIMAL	ZOO CITY
aardvark	Houston
bear	Tacoma
cheetah	San Diego
elephant	Omaha
zebra	Detroit

The cheetah is in the San Diego zoo (3). The Tacoma zoo doesn't have the aardvark, the elephant, or the zebra (1), so it has the bear. The Houston zoo doesn't have the zebra (2) or the elephant (4), so it has the aardvark. The elephant is not in the Detroit zoo (4), so it is in the Omaha zoo, and the Detroit zoo has the zebra.

11.

FIRST NAME	LAST NAME
Art	Ingram
Bob	King
Cathy	Green
Debbie	Lathem
Harold	Jones

There are two women and three men. Jones is a man (1) and is older than the other two men (1). Since Jones is younger than Green (1), Green is a woman who is older than any of the men. Debbie is younger than one of the men (2), so Debbie isn't Green. Then Cathy is Green.

King isn't Debbie, Harold or Art (2), so he is Bob. Then both Harold (2) and Jones (1) are older than the other two men, so Harold is Jones.

Debbie is older than Art (2), and Lathem is older than Ingram (3), so Debbie is Lathem, and Art is Ingram.

12.

FIRST NAME	LAST NAME	JOB
Antonia	Kennedy	biologist
Colleen	Shaw	magician
Emmanuel	Dewey	plasterer
Gustave	Hamilton	flight attendant

Shaw, a female (3), is not Antonia (3), so she is Colleen. Emmanuel is not Kennedy or Hamilton (2), so he is Dewey.

The flight attendant, a male (1), isn't Emmanuel Dewey (1), so he is Gustave. His last name is not Kennedy (1), so it is Hamilton, and so Antonia is Kennedy. The plasterer is not Shaw (3) or Kennedy (4, Antonia), so he is Dewey. Kennedy is not the magician (2), so Shaw is, and Kennedy is the biologist.

13.

FIRST NAME	LAST NAME	MONTH
Alexander	Loring	January
Bertha	Tyndall	February
Glenn	Silverman	May
Hiroko	Kraft	October

The person born in October is not Loring (2), Silverman (3), or Tyndall (1), so he or she is Kraft. Tyndall, not born in May (1) or January (3), was born in February. Loring, not born in May (2), was born in January. Then Silverman was born in May.

Loring, born in January, is not Glenn or Hiroko (1) or Bertha (2), so Loring is Alexander. Tyndall is not Glenn or Hiroko (1), so Tyndall is Bertha. Kraft, born in October, is not Glenn (1), so Kraft is Hiroko, and then Silverman is Glenn.

14.

FIRST NAME	LAST NAME	ITEM
Annette	Preston	slacks
Carlo	Oliver	gloves
Duane	Menzotti	jacket
Edith	Northrop	bathing suit

The three people in clue 1 all know each other, but there are at least two of the four people whom Duane doesn't know (2), so Duane is the fourth person. Similarly, Duane is not any of the people in clue 3. Then Duane isn't Oliver (1), Preston (3), or Northrop (2), so he is Menzotti. He didn't buy the bathing suit (1), the gloves (3), or the slacks (2), so he bought the jacket.

Oliver isn't Annette (1) or Edith (3), so Oliver is Carlo. Edith isn't Preston (3), so Annette is, and so Edith is Northrop.

Neither Annette nor Carlo Oliver bought the bathing suit (1), so Edith did. Preston didn't buy the gloves (3) so Oliver did, and so Preston bought the slacks.

EXAMPLES AND STEP-BY-STEP PROCEDURES

A Mind Bender® problem gives you two or more lists of things and asks you to match each item in one list with an item in the other list. Finding answers is easier if a chart is made showing all the lists at once and is then filled in. Note that the number of small boxes (within one large box) is the square of the number of things in any one list (Example 1 has three things in each list, so each large box has 9 small boxes).

TWO-DIMENSIONAL PROBLEMS

EXAMPLE 1

Problem: Davis, Edwards, and Jones are an astronaut, a computer programmer, and a skin diver.

1. Davis is not the astronaut or the computer programmer.

2. Jones is not the astronaut.

What does each person do?

Solution:

First, make the chart. Now use the first clue: Mark "1" (referring to clue 1) in D/A and D/CP. This leaves only one blank space in the "SD" row, so X it in.

	A	CP	SD
D	1	1	X
E			
J			

Now the "SD" column will have no more entries, so fill in the blank spaces there.

	A	CP	SD
D	1	1	X
E			SD
J			SD

We are through with the first clue, so now we can use the second clue.

	A	CP	SD
D	1	1	X
E			SD
J	2		SD

The "A" column now has only one blank space, so we X it. (The "J" row also has only one blank space, so we could have X'd it instead. It is a good idea to work on only one row or column at a time, so we choose **either** the "A" column **or** the "J" row to work on. When we finish with that one, then we start on the other one.)

	A	CP	SD
D	1	1	X
E	X		SD
J	2		SD

Fill in the remaining blank space in the "E" row.

	A	CP	SD
D	1	1	X
E	X	E	SD
J	2		SD

There is only one space remaining, so we X it.

The chart now shows the solution: Davis is the skin diver, Edwards is the astronaut, and Jones is the computer programmer.

	A	CP	SD
D	1	1	X
E	X	E	SD
J	2	X	SD

EXAMPLE 2

Problem: Davis, Edwards, Farman, and Jones are an astronaut, a bookbinder, a computer programmer, and a skin diver. Find each person's job.

1. Neither Edwards nor Jones knows anything about computers.

2. Neither Davis nor Edwards can swim.

Solution:

1. Make the chart and use *clue 1*. (Astronauts have to know something about computers, and so do computer programmers. So Edwards is not the astronaut or the computer programmer, and neither is Jones.)

	A	B	CP	SD
D				
E	1		1	
F				
J	1		1	

2. There is more than one blank space left in each column and row, so we can't do anything more from *clue 1*. So we use *clue 2*. (Astronauts and skin divers have to know how to swim, so Davis is not the astronaut or the skin diver, and neither is Edwards.)

	A	B	CP	SD
D	2			2
E	1		1	2
F				
J	1		1	

3. There is only one space left in the "E" row, so we X it in.

	A	B	CP	SD
D	2			2
E	1	X	1	2
F				
J	1		1	

4. The "B" column is matched up now, so we fill in the rest of the blank spaces here.

	A	B	CP	SD
D	2	B		2
E	1	X	1	2
F		B		
J	1	B	1	

5. Now we X the only blank space in the "D" row.

	A	B	CP	SD
D	2	B	X	2
E	1	X	1	2
F		B		
J	1	B	1	

6. The "CP" column is matched now, so fill in the remaining blank.

	A	B	CP	SD
D	2	B	X	2
E	1	X	1	2
F		B	CP	
J	1	B	1	

7. The "J" row isn't matched yet, and there is only one blank left. So we X this blank.

	A	B	CP	SD
D	2	B	X	2
E	1	X	1	2
F		B	CP	
J	1	B	1	X

8. Now the "SD" column is matched, so we fill in the blank there.

	A	B	CP	SD
D	2	B	X	2
E	1	X	1	2
F		B	CP	SD
J	1	B	1	X

9. Finally, the only blank left is in the "F" row and "A" column. Neither the row nor the column is matched yet, so we X this blank.

	A	B	CP	SD
D	2	B	X	2
E	1	X	1	2
F	X	B	CP	SD
J	1	B	1	X

We now have the solution: Davis, computer programmer; Edwards, bookbinder; Farman, astronaut; Jones, skin diver.

Sometimes the clues are not so obvious.

EXAMPLE 3

Problem: Davis, Edwards, Farman, and Jones are an astronaut, a bookbinder, a computer programmer, and a skin diver. Find each person's job and sex.

1. Davis and her husband invited the bookbinder and his wife to dinner.

2. The computer programmer said he enjoys playing chess with Farman.

3. The skin diver congratulated Jones on her bowling score of 230 last night.

Solution:

If we simply make a chart and fill it in from the obvious clues, we have: *clue 1*, Davis is not the bookbinder; *clue 2*, Farman is not the computer programmer; *clue 3*, Jones is not the skin diver. So our chart looks like the one at the right, and we may think that the problem does not give enough information for a solution.

	A	B	CP	SD
D		1		
E				
F			2	
J				3

But wait. *Clue 1* says "Davis and **her** husband," so Davis is a female. (Mark "F" for "female" in the margin.) And *Clue 1* says "bookbinder and **his** wife," so the bookbinder is a male. (Mark "M" for "male" in the margin.)

M_1				
	A	B	CP	SD
F_1 D		1		
E				
F				
J				

In *clue 2*, "he" is the computer programmer. And we already know that *clue 2* says Farman is not the computer programmer.

		M_1	M_2	
	A	B	CP	SD
F_1 D		1		
E				
F			2	
J				

Now the margins show Davis is a female and the computer programmer is a male, so Davis is not the computer programmer. We mark "FM" for "female-male" in the D/CP blank.

		M_1	M_2	
	A	B	CP	SD
F_1 D		1	FM	
E				
F			2	
J				

Now we are ready for *clue 3*. Here, "her" refers to Jones, so Jones is a female. We mark the margin. And we already know that *clue 3* says Jones is not the skin diver.

		M_1	M_2	
	A	B	CP	SD
F_1 D		1	FM	
E				
F			2	
F_3 J				3

Now Jones is a female, but the bookbinder and the computer programmer are males, so we fill in the blanks for J/B and for J/CP.

		M_1	M_2	
	A	B	CP	SD
F_1 D		1	FM	
E				
F			2	
F_3 J		FM	FM	3

There is only one blank left in the "CP" column, so we X it. It falls in the "E" row, so we also fill in the rest of the "E" row.

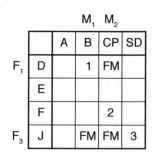

		M_1	M_2	
	A	B	CP	SD
F_1 D		1	FM	
E	E	E	X	E
F			2	
F_3 J		FM	FM	3

Now there is only one blank left in the "B" column, so we X it. It falls in the "F" row, so we also fill in the rest of this row.

		A	B	CP	SD
F₁	D		1	FM	
	E	E	E	X	E
	F	F	X	2	F
F₃	J		FM	FM	3

This leaves only one blank in the "SD" column, so we X this blank. Since this X is in the "D" row, we fill in the rest of the row, too.

		A	B	CP	SD
F₁	D	D	1	FM	X
	E	E	E	X	E
	F	F	X	2	F
F₃	J		FM	FM	3

We now have only one blank left, so we X it.

So the solution to the problem is this: Davis, skin diver, female; Edwards, computer programmer, male; Farman, bookbinder, male; Jones, astronaut, female.

		A	B	CP	SD
F₁	D	D	1	FM	X
	E	E	E	X	E
	F	F	X	2	F
F₃	J	X	FM	FM	3

EXAMPLE 4

Problem: Davis, Edwards, Farman, and Jones are an astronaut, a bookbinder, a computer programmer, and a skin diver. Find each person's job and sex.

1. Edwards is the bookbinder's son. (See note below.)

2. Jones's husband played golf with the computer programmer's husband.

3. The astronaut said Farman told her that he's going to Hawaii next month.

Note for *clue 1*: Since a son usually has the same last name as his father, this clue might lead you to think that the bookbinder must be a woman. However, the father may have adopted the son and so the two may have different last names.

Solution:

(Before reading this solution, see if you can solve the problem yourself.)

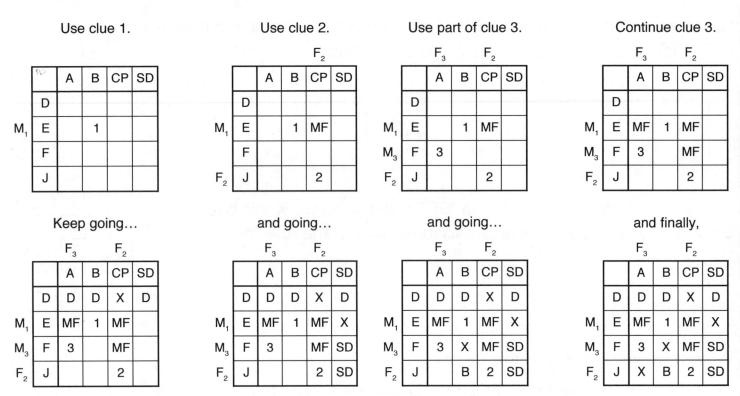

| Use clue 1. | Use clue 2. | Use part of clue 3. | Continue clue 3. |

So the solution to the problem is this: Davis, computer programmer, female; Edwards, skin diver, male; Farman, bookbinder, male; Jones, astronaut, female.

Sometimes a problem will include a clue in the general information instead of in a numbered item.

EXAMPLE 5

Problem: Two men and two women (Davis, Edwards, Farman, and Jones) are an astronaut, a bookbinder, a computer programmer, and a skin diver. Find each person's job and sex.

1. Edwards is the bookbinder's son.

2. The bookbinder is the computer programmer's son.

3. Farman is not a woman.

4. Jones and the skin diver are married.

5. Davis is not the astronaut.

Solution:

(Try to do this one yourself before reading the solution.)

Use clue 1.

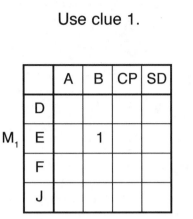

	A	B	CP	SD
D				
M₁ E		1		
F				
J				

Use the obvious part of clue 2.

M₂

	A	B	CP	SD
D				
M₁ E		1		
F				
J				

By combining clues 1 and 2, we see that Edwards must be the computer programmer's grandson.

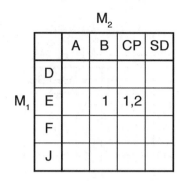

M₂

	A	B	CP	SD
D				
M₁ E		1	1,2	
F				
J				

The general information says two of the people are men and two are women. So far we know that Edwards and the bookbinder are the two men. But Edwards is not the computer programmer, so the computer programmer must be a woman.

M₂   F₂

	A	B	CP	SD
D				
M₁ E		1	1,2	
F				
J				

Use *clue 3*. Since Farman is not a woman, Farman is a man.

M₂   F₂

	A	B	CP	SD
D				
M₁ E		1	1,2	
M₃ F			MF	
J				

But now both Edwards and Farman are men, so Davis and Jones are women.

M₂   F₂

	A	B	CP	SD
F₃ D		FM		
M₁ E		1	1,2	
M₃ F			MF	
F₃ J		FM		

We now X the only blank left in the "B" column. This matches up in the "F" row, so we fill in the rest of the "F" row.

M₂   F₂

	A	B	CP	SD
F₃ D		FM		
M₁ E		1	1,2	
M₃ F	F	X	MF	F
F₃ J		FM		

Use *clue 4*. Since Jones is female, the skin diver must be male.

Clue 4, step 1

			M_2	F_2	M_4
		A	B	CP	SD
F_3	D		FM		
M_1	E			1	1,2
M_3	F	F	X	MF	F
F_3	J		FM		

Clue 4, step 2

			M_2	F_2	M_4
		A	B	CP	SD
F_3	D		FM		FM
M_1	E			1	1,2
M_3	F	F	X	MF	F
F_3	J		FM		FM

Since only two of the jobs are held by men, the astronaut must be a woman.

Clue 4, step 3

		F_4	M_2	F_2	M_4
		A	B	CP	SD
F_3	D		FM		FM
M_1	E			1	1,2
M_3	F	F	X	MF	F
F_3	J		FM		FM

Clue 4, step 4

		F_4	M_2	F_2	M_4
		A	B	CP	SD
F_3	D		FM		FM
M_1	E	MF		1	1,2
M_3	F	F	X	MF	F
F_3	J		FM		FM

Clue 4, step 5

		F_4	M_2	F_2	M_4
		A	B	CP	SD
F_3	D		FM		FM
M_1	E	MF		1	1,2 X
M_3	F	F	X	MF	F
F_3	J		FM		FM

Now we use *clue 5*.

Clue 5, step 1

		F_4	M_2	F_2	M_4
		A	B	CP	SD
F_3	D	5	FM		FM
M_1	E	MF		1	1,2 X
M_3	F	F	X	MF	F
F_3	J		FM		FM

Clue 5, step 2

		F_4	M_2	F_2	M_4
		A	B	CP	SD
F_3	D	5	FM	X	FM
M_1	E	MF		1	1,2 X
M_3	F	F	X	MF	F
F_3	J		FM		FM

Clue 5, step 3

		F_4	M_2	F_2	M_4
		A	B	CP	SD
F_3	D	5	FM	X	FM
M_1	E	MF		1	1,2 X
M_3	F	F	X	MF	F
F_3	J		FM	CP	FM

Clue 5, step 4

		F_4	M_2	F_2	M_4
		A	B	CP	SD
F_3	D	5	FM	X	FM
M_1	E	MF		1	1,2 X
M_3	F	F	X	MF	F
F_3	J	X	FM	CP	FM

Our solution is the same as for the previous problem: Davis, computer programmer, female; Edwards, skin diver, male; Farman, bookbinder, male; Jones, astronaut, female.

THREE-DIMENSIONAL PROBLEMS

To solve a three-dimensional problem, we make the chart so that each item in each list can be compared with each item in both other lists.

EXAMPLE 1

Problem: Davis, Edwards, and Farman are an astronaut, a bookbinder, and a skin diver. Their ages are 25, 30, and 35. Match each person's name, job, and age.

1. Davis is younger than the astronaut but older than Farman.

2. The skin diver is younger than the bookbinder.

Solution: To help keep our thinking straight on clue 1, we'll write in mathematical symbols: F < D < A. Then Farman is the youngest, Davis is in the middle, and the astronaut is the oldest. So Farman is 25, Davis is 30, and the astronaut is 35.

It is important to notice here that if the puzzle involved four people instead of three, we could not say that Farman is the youngest or that the astronaut is the oldest. The most we could say is (1) Farman is not either of the two oldest people, (2) Davis is not either the oldest or the youngest person, and (3) the astronaut is not either of the two youngest people. Let's look at how the chart works for this kind of problem.

Clue 1, step 1

	A	B	SD	25	30	35
D	1				X	
E						
F	1		X			
25						
30						
35	X					

Clue 1, step 2

	A	B	SD	25	30	35
D	1			25	X	D
E				25	30	
F	1			X	F	F
25	A					
30	A					
35	X	35	35			

Clue 1, step 3

	A	B	SD	25	30	35
D	1			25	X	D
E	X	E	E	25	30	X
F	1			X	F	F
25	A					
30	A					
35	X	35	35			

Clue 2 says the skin diver is younger than the bookbinder. The chart (from *clue 1, step 3*) says that Edwards, the astronaut, is 35. This leaves ages 25 and 30. So the skin diver is 25 and the bookbinder is 30. But we know from the chart that Farman is 25 and Davis is 30. So Farman is the skin diver and Davis is the bookbinder.

	A	B	SD	25	30	35
D	1	X	SD	25	X	D
E	X	E	E	25	30	X
F	1	F	X	X	F	F
25	A		25	X		
30	A		X	SD		
35	X	35	35			

Solution: Davis, bookbinder, 30; Edwards, astronaut, 35; Farman, skin diver, 25.

EXAMPLE 2

Problem: Davis, Edwards, Farman, and Gurley are an astronaut, a bookbinder, a plumber, and a skin diver. Their first names are Harold, Jenny, Ken, and Laura. Match up each person's full name and job.

1. Farman and the astronaut joined the same fraternity in college.

2. Edwards said she'd teach Jenny how to swim.

3. Ken asked the plumber if he could install a solar heating system for him.

4. Davis enjoys her work.

Solution: (Can you solve this one before reading the solution below?)

Clue 1

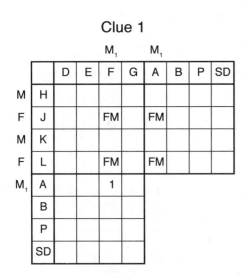

		D	E	F	G	A	B	P	SD
M	H								
F	J			FM		FM			
M	K								
F	L			FM		FM			
M_1	A			1					
	B								
	P								
	SD								

(M_1 over F column; M_1 over A column)

Clue 2

		D	E	F	G	A	B	P	SD
M	H		MF						
F	J		2	FM		FM			2
M	K		MF						
F	L	L	X	FM	L	FM			
M_1	A		MF	1					
	B								
	P								
	SD								

(F_2 over E column; M_1 over F column; M_1 over A column)

Clue 3, step 1

		D	E	F	G	A	B	P	SD
M	H		MF			H	H	X	H
F	J		2	FM		FM		FM	2
M	K		MF					3	
F	L	L	X	FM	L	FM		FM	
M_1	A		MF	1					
	B								
M_3	P		MF						
	SD								

(F_2 over E column; M_1 over F column; M_1 over A column; M_3 over P column)

Clue 3, step 2

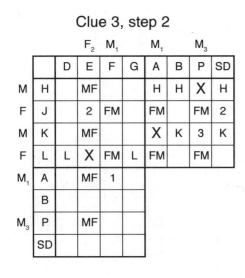

		D	E	F	G	A	B	P	SD
M	H		MF			H	H	X	H
F	J		2	FM		FM		FM	2
M	K		MF			X	K	3	K
F	L	L	X	FM	L	FM		FM	
M_1	A		MF	1					
	B								
M_3	P		MF						
	SD								

(F_2 over E column; M_1 over F column; M_1 over A column; M_3 over P column)

Clue 3, step 3*

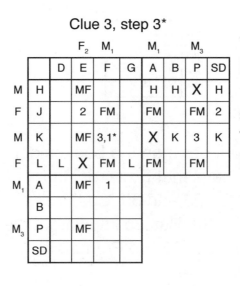

		D	E	F	G	A	B	P	SD
M	H		MF			H	H	X	H
F	J		2	FM		FM		FM	2
M	K		MF	3,1*		X	K	3	K
F	L	L	X	FM	L	FM		FM	
M_1	A		MF	1					
	B								
M_3	P		MF						
	SD								

(F_2 over E column; M_1 over F column; M_1 over A column; M_3 over P column)

*The "F" column says Farman is not the astronaut *(clue 1)*. But step 2 of *clue 3* says Ken is the astronaut. Therefore, Ken is not Farman.

3 1170 00685 9767

Clue 3, step 4

Column gender labels: E = F₂, F = M₁, A = M₁, P = M₃

	D	E	F	G	A	B	P	SD
M	H		MF			H	H	X
F	J		2	FM		FM	X	FM
M	K		MF	3,1		X	K	3
F	L	L	X	FM	L	FM	B	FM
M₁ (A)	A		MF	1					
(B)									
M₃ (P)	P		MF						
(SD)									

(M row SD = H; F row SD = 2; M row SD = K; F row SD = X)

Clue 3, step 5

Column gender labels: E = F₂, F = M₁, A = M₁, P = M₃

	D	E	F	G	A	B	P	SD
M	H	H	MF	X	H	H	H	X
F	J		2	FM		FM	X	FM
M	K		MF	3,1		X	K	3
F	L	L	X	FM	L	FM	B	FM
M₁ (A)	A		MF	1				
(B)								
M₃ (P)	P		MF					
(SD)								

(M row SD = H; F row SD = 2; M row SD = K; F row SD = X)

Clue 3, step 6

Column gender labels: E = F₂, F = M₁, A = M₁, P = M₃

	D	E	F	G	A	B	P	SD
M	H	H	MF	X	H	H	H	X
F	J		2	FM		FM	X	FM
M	K		MF	3,1		X	K	3
F	L	L	X	FM	L	FM	B	FM
M₁ (A)	A		MF	1				
(B)					F			
M₃ (P)	P	P	MF	X	P			
(SD)				F				

(M row SD = H; F row SD = 2; M row SD = K; F row SD = X)

Clue 3, step 7

Column gender labels: E = F₂, F = M₁, A = M₁, P = M₃

	D	E	F	G	A	B	P	SD
M	H	H	MF	X	H	H	H	X
F	J		2	FM		FM	X	FM
M	K		MF	3,1		X	K	3
F	L	L	X	FM	L	FM	B	FM
M₁ (A)	A		MF	1				
(B)			E	F				
M₃ (P)	P	P	MF	X	P			
(SD)	SD	SD	X	F	SD			

(M row SD = H; F row SD = 2; M row SD = K; F row SD = X)

Clue 4, step 1

Column gender labels: D = F₄, E = F₂, F = M₁, A = M₁, P = M₃

	D	E	F	G	A	B	P	SD
M	H	H	MF	X	H	H	H	X
F	J	X	2	FM	J	FM	X	FM
M	K	MF	MF	3,1		X	K	3
F	L	L	X	FM	L	FM	B	FM
M₁ (A)	A		MF	1				
(B)			E	F				
M₃ (P)	P	P	MF	X	P			
(SD)	SD	SD	X	F	SD			

(M row SD = H; F row SD = 2; M row SD = K; F row SD = X)

Clue 4, step 2

Column gender labels: D = F₄, E = F₂, F = M₁, A = M₁, P = M₃

	D	E	F	G	A	B	P	SD
M	H	H	MF	X	H	H	H	X
F	J	X	2	FM	J	FM	X	FM
M	K	MF	MF	3,1		X	K	3
F	L	L	X	FM	L	FM	B	FM
M₁ (A)	A	D	MF	1				
(B)	B	X	E	F	B			
M₃ (P)	P	P	MF	X	P			
(SD)	SD	SD	X	F	SD			

(M row SD = H; F row SD = 2; M row SD = K; F row SD = X)

Clue 4, step 3

Column gender labels: D = F₄, E = F₂, F = M₁, A = M₁, P = M₃

	D	E	F	G	A	B	P	SD
M	H	H	MF	X	H	H	H	X
F	J	X	2	FM	J	FM	X	FM
M	K	MF	MF	3,1	X	X	K	3
F	L	L	X	FM	L	FM	B	FM
M₁ (A)	A	D	MF	1	X			
(B)	B	X	E	F	B			
M₃ (P)	P	P	MF	X	P			
(SD)	SD	SD	X	F	SD			

(M row SD = H; F row SD = 2; M row SD = K; F row SD = X)

The solution is this: Harold Farman, plumber; Jenny Davis, bookbinder; Ken Gurley, astronaut; Laura Edwards, skin diver